To my husband Robert, who has been my biggest supporter as I tried on my new author hat. To my brother David, who told me I would never know if I could hit a home run if I didn't swing the bat first. To my daughters Giada and Lucia, along with my godson David Jr., who are my "smallest blessings" in life that make my world complete. To my parents Judy and Ben, for prompting my journey to URI. And to my extended family, my in-law family, numerous friends, and colleagues for making me smile each and every day.

www.mascotbooks.com

For more information, please contact:
Mascot Books
560 Herndon Parkway #120
Herndon, VA 20170
info@mascotbooks.com

CPSIA Code: PRT0116A
ISBN: 978-1-63177-306-8

Printed in the United States

RHODY® RAM'S

RHODE ISLAND® ADVENTURE

written by

Kerri E. Lanzieri

illustrated by

Rachel Schwarting

At Mascot College Rhody® Ram proudly wore white and **Keaney** blue,
The heart and soul of URI®—this was very true!

An assignment was given to mascots throughout the nation,
"Which college town is the best vacation destination?"

Deep in thought brainstorming, Rhody® closed one eye,
He wanted to give this contest his best college try.

He wanted to show his mascot pals how Rhode Island is really great,
But could Rhody® pull it off, being from the smallest state?

He could teach the URI® fight song, always the preferred cheer.
The thunderous chants echoed at every game in everyone's ear.

The loudest chants are heard at every basketball game.
With good sportsmanship, "Go Rams™!" fans proclaim.

He could show candid videos of new freshmen in the **Memorial Union,**

UNIVERSITY OF RHODE ISLAND

And weekend gatherings on the **Quad** for an alumni reunion!

He'd tell how the freshmen he meets every fall,
Grow into seniors ready to give the world their all!

They'd walk the scenic shore, filling their pockets with various shells,
Then quench their thirst at the frozen lemonade truck known simply as **"Del's."**

He'd gather them into a trolley stopping first at the **Narragansett Towers,**
Where they'd take in the sun and smell the gorgeous flowers.

Before flying kites at breezy **Beavertail** they'd zip up their coats,
And later stop in **Galilee** for fresh dinner from incoming boats.

Lobster, clams, white chowder, and clam cakes!
Caught fresh locally with poles, baskets, and rakes!

The next morning they'd ferry to an island known as **"The Block"** And marvel at the lighthouses with their 1800's wood and rock!

The Newport mansions were next to admire,
Then a short ride to the capital for **Providence WaterFire!**

They'd stop in **Federal Hill** for a tasty Italian treat,

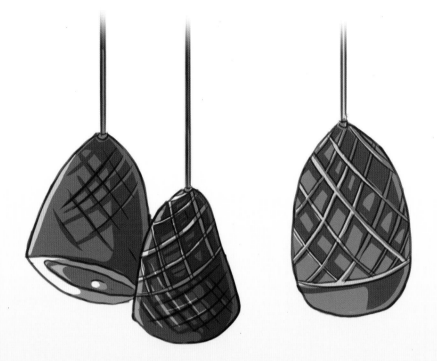

The official state appetizer, **calamari**, is a must-eat!

They can shop to their heart's content at the mall **Providence Place**,
And watching a **Bruins** hockey game, they're guaranteed an exciting ice chase!

For a bit of theatrics, how about **PPAC** for a Broadway show?
And to the **Roger Williams Park Zoo** all animal-lovers must go!

Rhody® proudly proclaimed, "It's easy to see
The smallest state is the best place to be!"

The Mascot professor was impressed with Rhody's Rhode Island vacation,
And declared **Kingston, Rhode Island** the best in the nation.

Rhody® learned that day when he took the top prize,
The very best things can be any shape or size!

About the Author

Kerri E. Lanzieri, LICSW, graduated with a B.S. from the University of Rhode Island and an M.S.W. from Simmons College in Boston. She is passionate about children's books because she uses them frequently in her work with students as a Rhode Island elementary school social worker. She started her journey of writing children's stories when her daughter's pet rabbit died suddenly and she needed just the right book to help her five year old in the grieving process. The stories she has written have an uplifting message or pertain to social/emotional topics which are tough for children to face.

Kerri, a proud Rhode Islander and URI® Alumni, lives with her husband Robert, daughters Giada and Lucia, and dog Fenway. She enjoys skiing, traveling, running, crafting, reading, writing, and spending time with family and friends.